First Learning

Alphabet

apple

cat

banana

Helpful hints for parents

- Start at the beginning of the book and try to work through the activities in order.
- Take time to talk about the activities together and make the sessions short and enjoyable.
- Make sure your child holds his or her pencil between thumb and forefinger, while resting the pencil on the middle finger. Remember, lightly, not tightly!
- Give help and lots of praise, rewarding your child by adding stickers to the reward chart for great work and effort.
- Practise saying the alphabet and learn the sounds the letters make.
- Once you have completed the workbook, move on to the practice pages bound in the centre.

Autumn Publishing

www.autumnchildrensbooks.co.uk

Alphabet

Trace over the letters of the alphabet.
Practise writing the alphabet on the lines.

a a   b b   c c   d d

e e   f f   g g   h h

i i   j j   k k

l l   m m   n n

oo pp qq

rr ss tt

uu vv ww xx

yy zz

First letter exercise

Look at the pictures. Say or write the first letter of each word.

_pple

_oat

_at

_og

_gg

_ish

_oat

_ouse

_gloo

_am

_ite

_emon

_ouse

Remember, think about the sound each missing letter makes.

 _ est

 _ range

 _ ig

 _ ueen

 _ abbit

 _ un

 _ iger

 _ mbrella

 _ iolin

 _ alrus

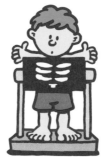 _ -ray

 _ o-yo

 _ ebra

Something beginning with 'f'

Colour the things in the picture that begin with **f**.

Look and match

Look at the pictures in each row. Circle each picture that is the same as the one in the first box.

Sort the shopping

Draw lines to put the shopping in the correct trolley.

Draw a picture of something that begins with **b** in the trolley.

Spelling maze

Help the boy through the maze to the treasure chest.
On the way you will spell his name.

Something beginning with 'r'

Colour the things that begin with **r**.

First letter sounds

Put a tick by the pictures that begin with the letters in the boxes.

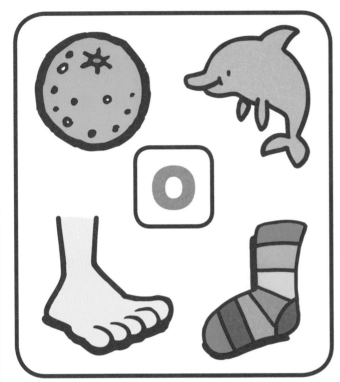

Middle letters

The middle letters are missing from these words.
Write the missing letters in the spaces. Look at the example.

Example:

c<u>a</u>t

b _ g

h _ t

w _ b

b _ d

h _ n

p _ g

s _ x

z _ p

c _ w

b _ y

d _ g

s _ n

j _ g

c _ p

Alphabet soup

Look at the letters in the alphabet soup.
Think of a word beginning with each letter.

Add the last letter

The last letter is missing from each of these words.
Write the missing letters in the spaces.

fro_

ca_

kin_

shee_

moo_

nes_

orang_

pea_

quee_

rabbi_

Alphabet practice

Write the letters of the alphabet on the lines.

a a   b b   c c   d d   e e   f f

g g   h h   i i   j j

k k   l l   m m   n n

o o   p p   q q

r r   s s   t t   u u

v v   w w   x x   y y   z z

First and last letters

1. Write the first letter of these different fruits.

_ear

_pple

_range

_anana

_emon

_rapes

_elon

_trawberry

2. Choose a letter to complete these words.

fea_

gla_

pi_

ja_

whe_

woo_

va_

Middle letters

Choose a letter to complete these words. In some cases, you can choose more than one of the letters and make more than one word.

a e i o u

b_d

p_sh

t_nt

st_r

r_ng

m_on

n_st

d_g

c_mb

c_r

fr_g

y_mmy

g_rl

s_n

Answers: bad, bed, bid, bud, tent, tint, rang, ring, rung, nest, comb, frog, girl, push, posh, star, stir, moon, dig, dog, dug, car, yummy, sin, son, sun

Letter draw

In the boxes, draw something that begins with each letter.

m

p

s

t

Little Lisa likes...

Little Lisa only likes things that begin with the letter **l**.
Colour the things that Lisa likes.

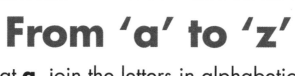

From 'a' to 'z'

Starting at **a**, join the letters in alphabetical order.

g

e
d
f
h
k
c
i
b
j
l
a
z
n
y
o
m
r
p
x
s
w
v
q
u
t

Spelling

Unscramble the letters to spell the words for these toys.
Write the words on the lines.

lodl

edytd

lbal

oy-oy

botro

nairt

Choose a letter

Choose the correct first letter to finish these words.
Write the letters on the lines.

d	b
dog

c	e
b_gg

c	s
c_up

y	g
yellow

m	v
_ase

a	i
_gloo

n	k
_ey

z	b
_ebra

p	n
_ig

Choose the correct last letter to finish these words.
Write the letters on the lines.

g   p

ju_

u   r

doo_

t   f

ha_

e   s

walru_

n   l

su_

c   g

fro_

m   t

goa_

s   n

quee_

t   p

zi_

Spot the sound

Draw a line from each letter to something in the big picture that begins with the same sound.

p	f	m	v	w	b

Amazing alphabet

Starting at **a**, trace the letters in alphabetical order and find your way through the maze.

start

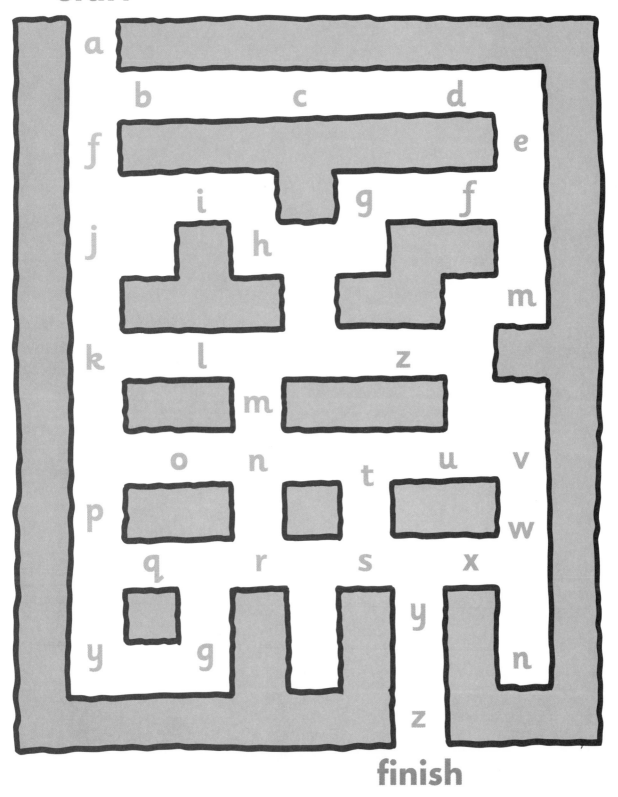

finish

Heads and tails

Look at the pictures at the beginning and end of each row.
Write the first letter of each picture. You will spell a three-letter word.

Example:

l   e   g

_   e   _

_   a   _

_   a   _

_   w   _

'S' sounds

The letter **s** has different sounds in some words. Look at the words in the sandcastle and write them in the correct buckets.

snake

nose   toys

sock   bees   us

noise

glass

mask   rose

s sounds   bus   **z sounds**

_____   _____

_____   toes   _____

_____   _____

_____   _____

_____   _____

You name it

Can you think of a name for each of these animals?
Each name must start with the same letter as the animal.
For example, a good name for a parrot would be Peter Parrot.

kangaroo

horse

zebra

monkey

dog

panda

Colour 'p'

Colour the things that begin with **p**.

More spot the sound

Draw a line from each letter to something in the picture that begins with the same sound.

c b p r l s

It's in your name

Colour the letters that are in your name.

a b c d e
f g h i j k
l m n o p
q r s t u
v w x y z

Congratulations!

You've finished the book.

Now you're ready to move on to the practice pages.

Answers

First letter exercise
apple, **b**oat, **c**at, **d**og, **e**gg, **f**ish, **g**oat, **h**ouse, **i**gloo, **j**am, **k**ite, **l**emon, **m**ouse, **n**est, **o**range, **p**ig, **q**ueen, **r**abbit, **s**un, **t**iger, **u**mbrella, **v**iolin, **w**alrus, **X**-ray, **y**o-yo, **z**ebra

Something beginning with 'f'
fire, fireman, fire engine, flag, farmer, fork, fish, frog, footprints, flower, fir tree, fly

Look and match
b
c
a
c

Sort the shopping
l – lamp, lemon
d – dress, doll
e – eggs, envelopes
c – cakes, carrots

Spelling maze

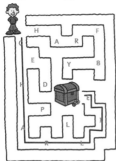

Something beginning with 'r'
robot, rocket, rabbit, rope, rake, ring, radio

First letter sounds
o – orange
r – rabbit
u – umbrella
x – X-ray

Middle letters
c**a**t, b**a**g, h**a**t, w**e**b, b**e**d, h**e**n, p**i**g, s**i**x, z**i**p, c**o**w, b**o**y, d**o**g, s**u**n, j**u**g, c**u**p

Add the last letter
fro**g**, ca**r**, kin**g**, shee**p**, moo**n**, nes**t**, orang**e**, pea**r**, quee**n**, rabbi**t**

Little Lisa likes...
lion, lemon, lizard, lolly

Spelling
lodl – doll
edytd – teddy
lbal – ball
oy-oy – yo-yo
botro – robot
nairt – train

Choose a letter
d – dog
e – egg
c – cup
y – yellow
v – vase
i – igloo
k – key
z – zebra
p – pig

g – jug
r – door
t – hat
s – walrus
n – sun
g – frog
t – goat
n – queen
p – zip

Spot the sound
p – paint, pencil, palette
f – flowers
m – mouse
v – vase
w – water
b – brush

Amazing alphabet

Heads and tails
be**d**, **f**a**n**, **t**a**p**, **o**w**l**

'S' sounds
s sounds – snake, bus, mask, sock, glass, us
z sounds – bees, toes, noise, rose, nose, toys
(Allow for regional variations)

Colour 'p'
pancakes, popcorn, pineapple, pizza, pear, peanuts, person

More spot the sound
c – cap
b – box, boy, bed, bat, blanket
p – pen, pillow, person
r – rug
l – lamp
s – sock, shoes